KS1 SATs

Grammar, Punctuation and Spelling

10-Minute Tests

Carol Matchett

Schofield & Sims

Introduction

This book contains 25 bite-sized tests to give you practice in answering grammar, punctuation and spelling questions quickly. There are 18 grammar and punctuation tests and seven spelling tests.

Each test is designed to be completed in 10 minutes.

The questions are just like the questions you will need to answer in the SATs Grammar, Punctuation and Spelling papers in Year 2.

What you will need

- a pencil
- an eraser
- a clock, watch or stopwatch
- an adult to time you, read out the spelling tests and mark the tests for you

How to use the book

Make sure that you are sitting in a quiet place where there aren't any distractions.

If you would like to start with a spelling test, turn to **Spelling Test 1** on page 4. If you would like to start with a grammar and punctuation test, turn to **Grammar and Punctuation Test 1** on page 6.

Spelling tests

Tell the adult when you are ready to begin. They will read the spellings in turn. Listen to the word you are being asked to spell. Then write it in the sentence.

Grammar and Punctuation tests

When you are ready to begin, ask the adult to start the timer.

Work through the questions in order. Read them carefully. Try to answer every question. If you get stuck on a question, leave it and move on to the next one.

When you reach the end of the test, stop and tell the adult that you have finished.

The adult will mark your test. Then the adult will fill in the **Total marks** section and, if it is a grammar and punctuation test, the **Time taken** section at the end of the test.

Turn to the **Progress chart** on page 54 or 55, depending on which type of test you took. Write your score in the box and colour the chart to show this score.

If you got some of the questions wrong, have another go at them before you look at the answers. Then ask the adult to check your work and help if you are still not sure.

You can use the **Tricky spellings record sheet** on page 56 to note down any spellings you find difficult.

Published by **Schofield & Sims Ltd**, 7 Mariner Court, Wakefield, West Yorkshire WF4 3FL, UK
Telephone 01484 607080
www.schofieldandsims.co.uk

This edition copyright © Schofield & Sims Ltd, 2019
First published in 2019
Second impression 2020

Author: **Carol Matchett**
Carol Matchett has asserted her moral rights under the Copyright, Designs and Patents Act, 1988, to be identified as the author of this work.

British Library Cataloguing in Publication Data
A catalogue record for this book is available from the British Library.

Design by **Ledgard Jepson**
Printed in the UK by **Page Bros (Norwich) Ltd**

ISBN 978 07217 1499 8

Contents

Spelling Test 1 4

Grammar and Punctuation Test 1 6

Grammar and Punctuation Test 2 8

Grammar and Punctuation Test 3 10

Spelling Test 2 12

Grammar and Punctuation Test 4 14

Grammar and Punctuation Test 5 16

Grammar and Punctuation Test 6 18

Spelling Test 3 20

Grammar and Punctuation Test 7 22

Grammar and Punctuation Test 8 24

Grammar and Punctuation Test 9 26

Spelling Test 4 28

Grammar and Punctuation Test 10 30

Grammar and Punctuation Test 11 32

Grammar and Punctuation Test 12 34

Spelling Test 5 36

Grammar and Punctuation Test 13 38

Grammar and Punctuation Test 14 40

Grammar and Punctuation Test 15 42

Spelling Test 6 44

Grammar and Punctuation Test 16 46

Grammar and Punctuation Test 17 48

Grammar and Punctuation Test 18 50

Spelling Test 7 52

Progress chart: grammar and punctuation tests 54

Progress chart: spelling tests 55

Tricky spellings record sheet 56

Notes for parents, teachers and other adult helpers

A pull-out answers section (pages A1 to A16) appears in the centre of this book, between pages 28 and 29. This provides answers to all the questions and scripts for the spelling tests, along with guidance on marking the papers. Remove the pull-out section before the child begins working through the tests.

Spelling Test 1

The adult who is helping you will read the sentences and tell you the missing words.

1 The news was a .... to us all.

1 mark

2 The frog sat on a ....

1 mark

3 The ladybird had a red ....

1 mark

4 Chloe .... me to play a game.

1 mark

5 The .... fox saw the red hen.

1 mark

6 I am .... than my friend Joe.

1 mark

7   The singer stood on the ....
1 mark

8   A .... landed in the jam.
1 mark

9   We are going to the zoo on ....
1 mark

10   I will .... you a letter.
1 mark

11   The little monster liked .... people.
1 mark

12   I like reading .... books best.
1 mark

Total marks ....

Grammar and Punctuation Test 1

1 Tick **one** word to complete the sentence below.

Vijay peeled the banana _____ ate it.

but ☐ or ☐ and ☐ when ☐

2 Which punctuation mark completes the sentence below?

What a really amazing story that was

Tick **one**.

a full stop ☐   a comma ☐

a question mark ☐   an exclamation mark ☐

3 Circle the **noun** in the sentence below.

I wore a scarf to keep warm.

4 Add a **suffix** to the word <u>paint</u> to complete the sentence below.

The children were paint_____ pictures of the sea.

5 What type of word is underlined in the sentence below?

I <u>put</u> the note in my pocket.

Tick **one**.

a noun ☐ an adjective ☐ a verb ☐ an adverb ☐

6   Why does the underlined word start with a **capital letter** in the sentence below?

Mum had a cup of coffee and <u>Adam</u> had some milk.

....

....

1 mark

7   Tick **one** box to show where a **comma** is needed in the sentence below.

Katie saw ants butterflies and bees in the garden.

1 mark

8   Which sentence is a **command**? Tick **one**.

This is the cloakroom.

Lunch boxes go on the trolley.

Hang your coat on the peg.

Is this your bag?

1 mark

9   Circle the correct **verbs** so that the sentence below is in the **past tense**.

Mum | smiles | smiled | and | calls | called | Raj's name.

1 mark

10   Write **one** sentence with the word <u>apple</u> in it.
Remember to use correct punctuation.

....

....

2 marks

Total marks ....   Time taken ....

Grammar and Punctuation Test **2**

1 Write the missing punctuation mark to complete the sentence below.

Is it going to rain today .... ☐

1 mark

2 Tick **one** word to complete the sentence below.

Kai always has a cup of tea .... he comes home.

because ☐   that ☐   when ☐   but ☐   ☐

1 mark

3 Add **two** letters to the word <u>lucky</u> to make a word that means <u>not lucky</u>.

I lost the game by just one point. I was very ....lucky. ☐

1 mark

4 What type of word is underlined in the sentence below?

Sharks have very <u>sharp</u> teeth.

Tick **one**.

a noun ☐   an adjective ☐   a verb ☐   an adverb ☐   ☐

1 mark

5 Look at where the arrow is pointing.

It was the day of the picnic Maddy was very excited.

↑

Which punctuation mark is needed? Tick **one**.

a comma ☐   an apostrophe ☐

a full stop ☐   a question mark ☐   ☐

1 mark

6 Circle the word that needs a **capital letter** in the sentence below.

Dad made the pizza and i helped to make the salad. ☐

1 mark

7 Draw lines to match the groups of words that have the same meaning. One has been done for you.

I am		couldn't
does not		I'm
could not		didn't
did not		doesn't

1 mark

8 Circle the **adverb** in the sentence below.

The   car   drove   slowly   down   the   road.

1 mark

9 Which sentence is a **statement**? Tick **one**.

I got a bike for my birthday. ☐

What a great present that is! ☐

What sort of bike is it? ☐

Tell me about your bike. ☐

1 mark

10 The verbs in boxes are in the present tense. Write these verbs in the **past tense**. One has been done for you.

I go ....went.......... to the beach with my family.

I make .... a sandcastle.

We play .... in the sea.

2 marks

Total marks .... Time taken ....

Grammar and Punctuation Test 3

1   Which is a complete sentence? Tick **one**.

The sun high in the sky. ☐

The sun is high in the sky. ☐

High in the sky. ☐

The sun high the sky. ☐

☐
1 mark

2   What type of word is underlined in the sentence below?

He watched a <u>plane</u> take off into the sky.

Tick **one**.

a verb ☐   an adverb ☐   a noun ☐   an adjective ☐

☐
1 mark

3   Add a **suffix** to the word <u>strong</u> to complete the sentence below.

The elephant was much strong............... than the little rabbit.

☐
1 mark

4   Tick **one** box to show where another **capital letter** is needed in the sentence below.

Luke and his family go on holiday every august.

☐   ☐   ☐   ☐

☐
1 mark

5   Tick **one** word so that the sentence below is in the **present tense**.

The birds are .... the berries.

peck ☐   pecking ☐   pecks ☐   pecked ☐

☐
1 mark

6 Add a **comma** to the sentence below in the correct place.

We grow vegetables fruit and herbs.

1 mark

7 Which sentence is an **exclamation**? The end punctuation is hidden. Tick **one**.

I heard you singing ☐

What a great singer you are ☐

What is your name ☐

How long have you been singing ☐

1 mark

8 Circle the **adjective** in the sentence below.

My rabbit likes to eat crunchy carrots.

1 mark

9 Which punctuation mark is needed in the sentence below?

I am Sams best friend.

Tick **one**.

a comma ☐   an exclamation mark ☐

an apostrophe ☐   a question mark ☐

1 mark

10 Tom has just finished reading a story. Write a **question** you could ask Tom about the story. Remember to use correct punctuation.

....

....

2 marks

Total marks ....   Time taken ....

Spelling Test 2

The adult who is helping you will read the sentences and tell you the missing words.

1   I must .... the fish their food.

2   The car began to .... off the road.

3   Jaye put on a .... and tie.

4   Ella had a .... about being famous.

5   I liked the .... pillow best.

6   There is no .... left in the car park.

7   I liked the .... of the book.

1 mark

8   Bees make .... in their hive.

1 mark

9   The wolf .... the house down.

1 mark

10   The town is full of .... at the weekend.

1 mark

11   Mum lit the .... on the cake.

1 mark

12   I made a .... mistake.

1 mark

Total marks ....

Grammar and Punctuation Test 4

1 Tick the **two** sentences that are **questions**. The end punctuation is hidden.

I have finished my lunch ☐

Have you had your lunch ☐

What is making all that noise ☐

What a noise that is ☐

1 mark

2 Tick **one** word to complete the sentence below.

Alex was looking for her friend Deepak .... she could not find him.

but ☐   if ☐   or ☐   that ☐

1 mark

3 Circle the word that needs a **capital letter** in the sentence below.

King   oliver   and   his   family   lived   in   a   big   palace.

1 mark

4 Circle the **verb** in the sentence below.

The   fly   buzzes   around   the   room.

1 mark

5 Which punctuation mark completes the sentence below?

What a brilliant footballer you are

Tick **one**.

a full stop ☐   a question mark ☐

a comma ☐   an exclamation mark ☐

1 mark

6 Add a **suffix** to the word <u>play</u> to complete the sentence below.

My new puppy is very play...................·

☐ 1 mark

7 What type of word is underlined in the sentence below?

The teacher spoke <u>quietly</u> to the class.

Tick **one**.

a noun ☐ an adjective ☐ a verb ☐ an adverb ☐

☐ 1 mark

8 Add **two full stops** in the correct places below.

Mia played football with her brother Pip watched them

☐ 1 mark

9 Tick **one** box to show where an **apostrophe** is needed in the sentence below.

Louis cant find his gloves anywhere.

☐ ☐ ☐ ☐

☐ 1 mark

10 The verbs in boxes are in the past tense. Write these verbs in the **present tense**. One has been done for you.

I | looked | ....look............. out of the window.

I | saw | .... my friend Billy.

He | waved | .... at me.

☐ 2 marks

Total marks .... Time taken ....

Grammar and Punctuation Test 5

1 Tick **one** word to complete the sentence below.

Nish was in bed .... he had a cold.

that ☐   or ☐   because ☐   if ☐

☐ 1 mark

2 Which punctuation mark completes the sentence below?

Did you know some birds can't fly

Tick **one**.

a full stop ☐   a question mark ☐

a comma ☐   an exclamation mark ☐

☐ 1 mark

3 Which sentence is a **command**? Tick **one**.

I am going to draw a picture. ☐

Pass me the red crayon. ☐

It is a picture of a sunset. ☐

Can you show me the picture? ☐

☐ 1 mark

4 What type of word is underlined in the sentence below?

Lois packed everything <u>neatly</u> into her rucksack.

Tick **one**.

a noun ☐   an adjective ☐   a verb ☐   an adverb ☐

☐ 1 mark

5 Why do the underlined words start with a **capital letter**?

On <u>Friday</u> afternoon, <u>Mrs Gill</u> went on the train to <u>Cardiff</u>.

....

....

☐ 1 mark

6 Tick the **two nouns** in the sentence below.

We can ride our new bikes in the park.

☐   ☐ ☐ ☐   ☐

1 mark

7 Write **s** or **es** to make each word a plural.

box...................   ball...................   bench...................

1 mark

8 Which sentence is correct? Tick **one**.

The dog ran to the pond and jump in. ☐

The dog ran to the pond and jumped in. ☐

The dog runs to the pond and jump in. ☐

The dog runs to the pond and jumped in. ☐

1 mark

9 Which phrase uses an **apostrophe** correctly? Tick **one**.

Jacks' shoes ☐   Jack's shoes ☐

Jacks shoes' ☐   Jacks shoe's ☐

1 mark

10 Write **one** sentence to describe something about a duck. Remember to use correct punctuation.

....

....

2 marks

Total marks ....   Time taken ....

Grammar and Punctuation Test 6

1 Which punctuation mark completes the sentence below?

How fast she ran to win the race

Tick **one**.

a full stop ☐   a question mark ☐

a comma ☐   an exclamation mark ☐

☐
1 mark

2 Circle the **two adjectives** in the sentence below.

Inside the cave it was dark and damp.

☐
1 mark

3 Read the sentences below. What type of sentence are they?

My dad makes me laugh. He tells funny jokes.

Tick **one**.

questions ☐   commands ☐

statements ☐   exclamations ☐

☐
1 mark

4 Add **two full stops** in the correct places below.

We played hide and seek in the hall Erin hid first

☐
1 mark

5 Tick **one noun phrase** below.

I dug and dug ☐   I found something ☐

a gold ring ☐   Dad was pleased ☐

☐
1 mark

6 Tick **one verb** in the sentence below.

On Friday, we had our breakfast early.

☐ ☐ ☐ ☐

☐
1 mark

7   Look at where the arrow is pointing.

I was in the same team as James Mohan and Luna when we played football.

Which punctuation mark is needed? Tick **one**.

a full stop ☐   an exclamation mark ☐

a comma ☐   an apostrophe ☐

☐

1 mark

8   Circle the correct **verbs** so that the sentences are in the **past tense**.

Two boats were | sailed | sails | sailing | out to sea. I was

| watched | watches | watching | them from the shore.

☐

1 mark

9   Why does the underlined word have an **apostrophe**?

Do you think it's going to snow today?

....

....

☐

1 mark

10   a) Add a **suffix** to the word fold to complete the sentence below.

I put all my work in a fold................ .

b) What type of word have you made by adding the suffix?
Tick **one**.

a verb ☐   an adverb ☐

a noun ☐   an adjective ☐

☐

2 marks

Total marks .... Time taken ....

Spelling Test **3**

The adult who is helping you will read the sentences and tell you the missing words.

1   I saw a mouse .... the cheese.

2   We had a .... at the weekend.

3   Jess was .... of her new bike.

4   I cut out .... to make a pattern.

5   I left my bag in the ....

6   It was as light as a ....

7   I had to .... to clean the floor.

1 mark

8   I used .... to draw the picture.

1 mark

9   The red light was a ....

1 mark

10   Mum will .... to work by bus today.

1 mark

11   The clown told the .... jokes.

1 mark

12   Nan was .... in the garden.

1 mark

Total marks ....

Grammar and Punctuation Test 7

1 Tick **one** word to complete the sentence below.

We must go now .... the shop will be shut.

and ☐   but ☐   or ☐   when ☐

☐
1 mark

2 Circle the **verb** in the sentence below.

It   feels   much   warmer   today.

☐
1 mark

3 Write the missing punctuation mark to complete the sentence below.

How do spiders make their webs..................

☐
1 mark

4 Draw a line to match each word to the **suffix** that turns it into a **noun**. You can use a suffix more than once.

Word   **Suffix**

| sad |

| excite | | ness |

| wicked | | ment |

☐
1 mark

5 Read the sentences below.

Turn the printer on.
Place the paper in the paper tray.
Press the print button.

Tick **one** word that describes all the sentences.

statements ☐   exclamations ☐

questions ☐   commands ☐

☐
1 mark

6 Which sentence uses **capital letters** correctly? Tick **one**.

Last year i went to the Fair for my birthday. ☐

Last year i went to the fair for my Birthday. ☐

Last year I went to the fair for my birthday. ☐

Last year I went to the Fair for my Birthday. ☐ ☐

1 mark

7 What type of word is underlined in the sentence below? Tick **one**.

We played on the <u>swings</u> and then had an ice cream.

a verb ☐ an adverb ☐ a noun ☐ an adjective ☐ ☐

1 mark

8 Tick to show whether each sentence is written in the **past tense** or the **present tense**.

Sentence	Past tense	Present tense
Mum cleans the windows.		
Dad washed the dishes.		
Khalid made his bed.		

☐

1 mark

9 Write an **apostrophe** in the correct place in the sentence below.

T h o s e   a r e   R y a n s   t o y s.

☐

1 mark

10 Ali has been to the safari park.

Write a **statement** about an elephant he sees there.
Remember to use correct punctuation.

....

....

☐

2 marks

Total marks .... Time taken ....

Grammar and Punctuation Test 8

1   What type of sentence is below? The end punctuation is hidden.

Can you shut the door

Tick **one**.

a statement ☐   a command ☐

an exclamation ☐   a question ☐   ☐

1 mark

2   What type of word is underlined in the sentence below?

Everyone knew that the queen was a <u>wise</u> woman.

Tick **one**.

a verb ☐   an adverb ☐   a noun ☐   an adjective ☐   ☐

1 mark

3   Add **two** letters to the word <u>lock</u> to make a word that means the opposite.

Dad used the key to .... lock the door.   ☐

1 mark

4   Circle the word that needs a **capital letter** in the sentence below.

This year I hope to visit my aunt in india.   ☐

1 mark

5   Which sentence uses an **exclamation mark** correctly? Tick **one**.

Do you like ice cream!   ☐

How creamy this ice cream is!   ☐

What flavour do you like best!   ☐

Can we have some more ice cream!   ☐   ☐

1 mark

6 Tick **one noun phrase** below.

very slowly ☐   was sleeping ☐

a little puppy ☐   really soft ☐

☐
1 mark

7 Circle the **adverb** in the sentence below.

Latif shared the cherries fairly with his brother

and sister.

☐
1 mark

8 Which sentence is correct? Tick **one**.

Dan held on to the rope and pull.   ☐

Dan held on to the rope and pulls.   ☐

Dan holds on to the rope and pull.   ☐

Dan holds on to the rope and pulls.   ☐

☐
1 mark

9 Write **one verb** to complete the sentence below.

The children were .... their books.

☐
1 mark

10 Write an **apostrophe** in the correct place in each of the sentences below.

a) Now Ive found lots of shells.

b) Dev plays marbles and hes good.

☐
2 marks

Total marks .... Time taken ....

Grammar and Punctuation Test 9

1 Tick **one** word to complete the sentence below.

Ice cream will melt .... you leave it in the sun.

if ☐ and ☐ so ☐ but ☐

1 mark

2 Which option is punctuated correctly? Tick **one**.

My brother likes grapes he has them for a snack ☐

My brother likes grapes he has them for a snack. ☐

My brother likes grapes. He has them for a snack. ☐

my brother likes grapes He has them for a snack. ☐

☐
1 mark

3 What type of word is underlined in the sentence below?

All of the streets in the town were <u>empty</u>.

Tick **one**.

a noun ☐   a verb ☐   an adjective ☐   an adverb ☐   ☐
1 mark

4 Look at the underlined parts of the words.

soft<u>ly</u>   play<u>er</u>   help<u>ful</u>   late<u>ness</u>

What is the name for this part of the word? Tick **one**.

tense ☐   plural ☐   suffix ☐   adverb ☐   ☐
1 mark

5 Add a **comma** to the sentence below in the correct place.

Collect some twigs grass and leaves from the garden.

☐
1 mark

6 Add a **full stop** or a **question mark** to complete each sentence below.

Are you coming to see the new slide................

There are five tents in the field................

Do you want to play cricket................

1 mark

7 Circle the **two nouns** in the sentence below.

I think I will put my chair under that tree over there.

1 mark

8 What type of sentence is below? The end punctuation is hidden.

What a lovely garden you have▪

a statement ☐   a question ☐

a command ☐   an exclamation ☐

1 mark

9 Tick to show whether each sentence is written in the **past tense** or the **present tense**.

Sentence	Past tense	Present tense
Mum was painting the fence.		
I am sweeping the path.		
Jo is looking for her football.		

1 mark

10 Write a **command** a teacher could say at the end of a lesson. Remember to use correct punctuation.

....

....

2 marks

Total marks ....   Time taken ....

Spelling Test 4

The adult who is helping you will read the sentences and tell you the missing words.

1 I saw a leaf .... on the water.
   1 mark

2 The pirate had a .... over her eye.
   1 mark

3 They sell lots of things at the ....
   1 mark

4 This jumper is .... than the red one.
   1 mark

5 Max was .... to finish the jigsaw.
   1 mark

6 We found a .... in the soil.
   1 mark

KS1 SATs Grammar, Punctuation and Spelling 10-Minute Tests

Notes for parents, teachers and other adult helpers

KS1 SATs Grammar, Punctuation and Spelling 10-Minute Tests are short, timed tests designed to build speed and confidence.

The questions in the tests closely match the questions children will need to answer in the Key Stage 1 SATs Grammar, Punctuation and Spelling papers, which are taken in Year 2. As children work through the book, the tests get progressively more challenging.

It is intended that children will take around 10 minutes to complete each test. However, SATs papers are not strictly timed at this age, so allow them longer if they need it.

How to use the book

Remove this pull-out section before giving the book to the child.

Before the child begins work on the first test, together read the instructions on page 2. As you do so, point out to the child that there is a target time of 10 minutes for completing the grammar and punctuation tests (the timing of the spelling tests may vary slightly depending on your reading speed). Make sure the child has all the equipment in the list headed **What you will need** on page 2.

Administering the grammar and punctuation tests

Be sure that the child knows to tell you clearly when they have finished the test.

When the child is ready, say 'Start the test now' and make a note of the start time.

When the child has finished, make a note of the end time and then work out how long they took to complete the test. Then fill in the **Time taken** section, which appears at the end of the test.

Administering the spelling tests

The spelling tests need to be read aloud to the child. The scripts for the seven spelling tests are provided in this pull-out section.

Before you begin the test, explain to the child that you are going to read some sentences. These sentences are printed on the test page but with a word missing. They have to write the missing word in the blank space.

Check your child knows what to do and has the book open to the correct test.

The 12 spellings should then be read aloud as follows:

> Give the spelling number (e.g. *Spelling 1*).
>
> Say: *The word is...*
>
> Read the context sentence provided in the script.
>
> Repeat: *The word is...*

Leave a gap of at least 12 seconds between spellings.

After the last spelling, read all 12 sentences again so your child can check and make any changes.

After the test

Mark the child's answers using this pull-out section. Each grammar and punctuation test is out of 11 marks and each spelling test is out of 12 marks. Most questions are worth 1 mark. For questions worth 2 marks, follow the advice on whether to award 0, 1 or 2 marks. No half marks can be awarded. Then complete the **Total marks** section at the end of the test.

Turn to the appropriate **Progress chart** on page 54 or 55. Encourage the child to write their score in the box and colour the chart to show this score.

Whatever the test score, always encourage the child to have another go at the questions that they got wrong – without looking at the answers. If the child's answers are still incorrect, work through these questions together.

If the child struggles with particular question types, help them to develop the strategies needed. The focus of each question is shown in blue under each answer to help you determine which aspects of grammar, punctuation or spelling need more practice.

Ask them to complete the next test at a later date, once they have had sufficient time to practise any question types they found difficult.

Spelling test transcripts

Spelling Test 1

Spelling 1
The word is **shock**.
The news was a **shock** to us all.
The word is **shock**.

Spelling 2
The word is **stone**.
The frog sat on a **stone**.
The word is **stone**.

Spelling 3
The word is **body**.
The ladybird had a red **body**.
The word is **body**.

Spelling 4
The word is **asked**.
Chloe **asked** me to play a game.
The word is **asked**.

Spelling 5
The word is **sly**.
The **sly** fox saw the red hen.
The word is **sly**.

Spelling 6
The word is **taller**.
I am **taller** than my friend Joe.
The word is **taller**.

Spelling 7
The word is **stage**.
The singer stood on the **stage**.
The word is **stage**.

Spelling 8
The word is **wasp**.
A **wasp** landed in the jam.
The word is **wasp**.

Spelling 9
The word is **Wednesday**.
We are going to the zoo on **Wednesday**.
The word is **Wednesday**.

Spelling 10
The word is **write**.
I will **write** you a letter.
The word is **write**.

Spelling 11
The word is **scaring**.
The little monster liked **scaring** people.
The word is **scaring**.

Spelling 12
The word is **fiction**.
I like reading **fiction** books best.
The word is **fiction**.

Spelling Test 2

Spelling 1
The word is **give**.
I must **give** the fish their food.
The word is **give**.

Spelling 2
The word is **skid**.
The car began to **skid** off the road.
The word is **skid**.

Spelling 3
The word is **shirt**.
Jaye put on a **shirt** and tie.
The word is **shirt**.

Spelling 4
The word is **dream**.
Ella had a **dream** about being famous.
The word is **dream**.

Spelling 5
The word is **softest**.
I liked the **softest** pillow best.
The word is **softest**.

Spelling 6
The word is **space**.
There is no **space** left in the car park.
The word is **space**.

Spelling 7
The word is **cover**.
I liked the **cover** of the book.
The word is **cover**.

Spelling 8
The word is **honey**.
Bees make **honey** in their hive.
The word is **honey**.

Spelling 9
The word is **blew**.
The wolf **blew** the house down.
The word is **blew**.

Spelling 10
The word is **shoppers**.
The town is full of **shoppers** at the weekend.
The word is **shoppers**.

Spelling 11
The word is **candle**.
Mum lit the **candle** on the cake.
The word is **candle**.

Spelling 12
The word is **careless**.
I made a **careless** mistake.
The word is **careless**.

Spelling test transcripts

Spelling Test 3

Spelling 1
The word is **sniff**.
I saw a mouse **sniff** the cheese.
The word is **sniff**.

Spelling 2
The word is **party**.
We had a **party** at the weekend.
The word is **party**.

Spelling 3
The word is **proud**.
Jess was **proud** of her new bike.
The word is **proud**.

Spelling 4
The word is **shapes**.
I cut out **shapes** to make a pattern.
The word is **shapes**.

Spelling 5
The word is **classroom**.
I left my bag in the **classroom**.
The word is **classroom**.

Spelling 6
The word is **feather**.
It was as light as a **feather**.
The word is **feather**.

Spelling 7
The word is **kneel**.
I had to **kneel** to clean the floor.
The word is **kneel**.

Spelling 8
The word is **chalk**.
I used **chalk** to draw the picture.
The word is **chalk**.

Spelling 9
The word is **warning**.
The red light was a **warning**.
The word is **warning**.

Spelling 10
The word is **travel**.
Mum will **travel** to work by
bus today.
The word is **travel**.

Spelling 11
The word is **funniest**.
The clown told the **funniest** jokes.
The word is **funniest**.

Spelling 12
The word is **busy**.
Nan was **busy** in the garden.
The word is **busy**.

Spelling Test 4

Spelling 1
The word is **float**.
I saw a leaf **float** on the water.
The word is **float**.

Spelling 2
The word is **patch**.
The pirate had a **patch** over her eye.
The word is **patch**.

Spelling 3
The word is **market**.
They sell lots of things at
the **market**.
The word is **market**.

Spelling 4
The word is **thicker**.
This jumper is **thicker** than the
red one.
The word is **thicker**.

Spelling 5
The word is **trying**.
Max was **trying** to finish the jigsaw.
The word is **trying**.

Spelling 6
The word is **worm**.
We found a **worm** in the soil.
The word is **worm**.

Spelling 7
The word is **while**.
We had to wait for a **while**.
The word is **while**.

Spelling 8
The word is **wreck**.
The diver found the **wreck** of a ship.
The word is **wreck**.

Spelling 9
The word is **crazy**.
Ben had this **crazy** idea.
The word is **crazy**.

Spelling 10
The word is **donkeys**.
I saw two **donkeys** in the field.
The word is **donkeys**.

Spelling 11
The word is **medal**.
He won the gold **medal** in the race.
The word is **medal**.

Spelling 12
The word is **measure**.
I used a ruler to **measure** the line.
The word is **measure**.

Spelling Test 5

Spelling 1
The word is **blink**.
The smoke made me **blink** my eyes.
The word is **blink**.

Spelling 2
The word is **bright**.
Amy likes to wear **bright** colours.
The word is **bright**.

Spelling 3
The word is **hear**.
I can **hear** something outside.
The word is **hear**.

Spelling 4
The word is **playground**.
The children ran into the **playground**.
The word is **playground**.

Spelling 5
The word is **crosses**.
Zara **crosses** the road at the lights.
The word is **crosses**.

Spelling 6
The word is **fridge**.
I put the milk in the **fridge**.
The word is **fridge**.

Spelling 7
The word is **month**.
Claire was born in the **month** of May.
The word is **month**.

Spelling 8
The word is **graph**.
We drew a **graph** to show the birds we saw.
The word is **graph**.

Spelling 9
The word is **watch**.
Mr Lewis looked at his **watch**.
The word is **watch**.

Spelling 10
The word is **puddle**.
The rain made a **puddle** on the floor.
The word is **puddle**.

Spelling 11
The word is **babies**.
All the **babies** began to cry.
The word is **babies**.

Spelling 12
The word is **graceful**.
The swan looked very **graceful**.
The word is **graceful**.

Spelling Test 6

Spelling 1
The word is **glue**.
This **glue** is very sticky.
The word is **glue**.

Spelling 2
The word is **weak**.
I felt **weak** when I was ill.
The word is **weak**.

Spelling 3
The word is **solve**.
It was a tricky problem to **solve**.
The word is **solve**.

Spelling 4
The word is **sketch**.
Ruby drew a **sketch** of her cat.
The word is **sketch**.

Spelling 5
The word is **drinking**.
I was **drinking** a glass of water.
The word is **drinking**.

Spelling 6.
The word is **fancy**.
We went to a **fancy** dress party.
The word is **fancy**.

Spelling 7
The word is **dripping**.
The tap was **dripping** into the bath.
The word is **dripping**.

Spelling 8
The word is **pencil**.
Write your name in **pencil**.
The word is **pencil**.

Spelling 9
The word is **squash**.
Don't **squash** the cake.
The word is **squash**.

Spelling 10
The word is **towards**.
Take three steps **towards** me.
The word is **towards**.

Spelling 11
The word is **hurried**.
The man **hurried** on to the train.
The word is **hurried**.

Spelling 12
The word is **people**.
Lots of **people** like dogs.
The word is **people**.

Spelling Test 7

Spelling 1
The word is **fizz**.
The mixture began to **fizz**.
The word is **fizz**.

Spelling 2
The word is **burst**.
The little boy **burst** his balloon.
The word is **burst**.

Spelling 3
The word is **knock**.
There was a **knock** at the door.
The word is **knock**.

Spelling 4
The word is **lolly**.
I would like a red ice **lolly**.
The word is **lolly**.

Spelling 5
The word is **limped**.
The girl **limped** over the line.
The word is **limped**.

Spelling 6
The word is **fry**.
You can **fry** fish in a pan.
The word is **fry**.

Spelling 7
The word is **upstairs**.
I went **upstairs** to bed.
The word is **upstairs**.

Spelling 8
The word is **kettle**.
Dad boiled the **kettle** to make tea.
The word is **kettle**.

Spelling 9
The word is **half**.
The bell rang at **half** past three.
The word is **half**.

Spelling 10
The word is **worth**.
How much is the picture **worth**?
The word is **worth**.

Spelling 11
The word is **carries**.
The woman **carries** the heavy case.
The word is **carries**.

Spelling 12
The word is **tasteless**.
The soup was **tasteless**.
The word is **tasteless**.

Answers

Grammar and punctuation tests

Grammar and Punctuation Test 1 (page 6)

1 and — **1 mark**
Co-ordinating conjunctions – *and*, *but*, *or*

2 an exclamation mark — **1 mark**
Exclamation marks to demarcate sentences

3 (scarf) — **1 mark**
Word classes – nouns

4 paint**ing** — **1 mark**
Suffixes added to verbs

5 a verb — **1 mark**
Word classes – verbs

6 1 mark for an answer that explains that *Adam* starts with a capital letter because it is a name. e.g.
It's a name.
Names always start with a capital letter.
Capital letters for names of people

7 Katie saw ants butterflies and bees in the garden. — **1 mark**
Commas to separate items in a list

8 Hang your coat on the peg. — **1 mark**
Commands – function and grammatical patterns

9 1 mark for both words correct
(smiled) (called)
Verb tenses – simple past tense

10 2 marks for an appropriate and complete sentence, which also starts with a capital letter and ends with a full stop (or question mark or exclamation mark, if that is appropriate). e.g.
I picked an apple off the tree.

1 mark for an appropriate and complete sentence with incorrect or missing punctuation. e.g.
the apple was ripe

0 marks for a phrase or incomplete sentence. e.g.
a nice red apple/I like apple

Combining words to make sentences

Sentence punctuation – capital letters and full stops (or ? or ! if appropriate)

Grammar and Punctuation Test 2 (page 8)

1 Is it going to rain today**?** — **1 mark**
Question marks to demarcate sentences

2 when — **1 mark**
Subordinating conjunctions – *when*, *if*, *that*, *because*

3 **un**lucky — **1 mark**
Prefixes – how *un–* changes verbs and adjectives

4 an adjective — **1 mark**
Word classes – adjectives

5 a full stop — **1 mark**
Full stops to demarcate sentences

6 (i) — **1 mark**
Capital letter for the word *I*

7 1 mark for all joined correctly

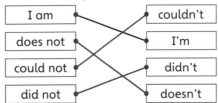

Apostrophes in contracted forms

8 (slowly) — **1 mark**
Word classes – adverbs

9 I got a bike for my birthday. — **1 mark**
Statements – function and grammatical patterns

10 1 mark for one correct word
2 marks for two correct words
Note: the words must be spelt correctly.
I **made** a sandcastle.
We **played** in the sea.
Verb tenses – simple past tense

Grammar and Punctuation Test 3 (page 10)

1 The sun is high in the sky. — **1 mark**
How words combine to make sentences

2 a noun — **1 mark**
Word classes – nouns

3 strong**er** — **1 mark**
Suffixes – forming adjectives using *–er* and *–est*

4 Luke and his family go on holiday every august. — **1 mark**
Capital letters for names of people and months of the year

5 pecking — **1 mark**
Verb tenses – progressive form of present tense

6 We grow vegetables, fruit and herbs. — **1 mark**
Commas to separate items in a list

7 What a great singer you are — **1 mark**
Exclamations – function and grammatical patterns

8 (crunchy) — **1 mark**
Word classes – adjectives

9 as apostrophe — **1 mark**
Apostrophe for possession

10 2 marks for an appropriate and correctly formed question, which also starts with a capital letter and ends with a question mark. e.g.
What was the story about?
How did it end?
Was it a good story?

Answers

Test 3 (page 10) continued

1 mark for an appropriate and correctly formed question, which does not have the necessary capital letter and/or question mark. e.g.
Is it a funny story.
what happened in the story?

0 marks if the sentence does not fit the context or does not make sense

Questions – function and grammatical pattern

Sentence punctuation – capital letters and question marks to demarcate question sentences

Grammar and Punctuation Test 4 (page 14)

1 **1 mark for both correctly identified**
Have you had your lunch
What is making all that noise
Questions – function and grammatical patterns

2 but   **1 mark**
Co-ordinating conjunctions – *and, but, or*

3 (oliver)   **1 mark**
Capital letters for names of people

4 (buzzes)   **1 mark**
Word classes – verbs

5 an exclamation mark   **1 mark**
Exclamation marks to demarcate sentences

6 play**ful**   **1 mark**
Suffixes – forming adjectives using *–ful* and *–less*

7 an adverb   **1 mark**
Word classes – adverbs

8 **1 mark for both full stops in the correct place**
Mia played football with her brother. Pip watched them.
Full stops to demarcate sentences

9 Louis cant find his gloves anywhere.
✓
        1 mark
Apostrophes in contracted forms

10 **1 mark for one correct word**
2 marks for two correct words
Note: the words must be spelt correctly.
I **see** my friend Billy.
He **waves** at me.
Verb tenses – simple present tense

Grammar and Punctuation Test 5 (page 16)

1 because   **1 mark**
Subordinating conjunctions – *when, if, that, because*

2 a question mark   **1 mark**
Question marks to demarcate sentences

3 Pass me the red crayon.   **1 mark**
Commands – function and grammatical patterns

4 an adverb   **1 mark**
Word classes – adverbs

5 **1 mark for an answer that explains that the words start with a capital letter because they are names.** e.g.
They are all names.
Friday, Mrs Gill and Cardiff are names.
A name needs a capital letter.
Capital letters for names of people, places and days of the week

6 **1 mark for both words correct**
We can ride our new bikes in the park.
       ✓   ✓
Word classes – nouns

7 **1 mark for all three correct**
box**es**   ball**s**   bench**es**
Plural noun suffixes *-s* or *-es*

8 The dog ran to the pond and jumped in.   **1 mark**
Tense consistency – simple past tense

9 Jack's shoes   **1 mark**
Apostrophe for possession

10 **2 marks for an appropriate and complete sentence, which also starts with a capital letter and ends with a full stop (or question mark or exclamation mark, if that is appropriate).** e.g.
I saw a duck on the pond.
The duck went quack.
Did you see the duck on the pond?

1 mark for an appropriate and complete sentence with incorrect or missing punctuation. e.g.
The duck ate the bread

0 marks for a phrase or incomplete sentence. e.g.
A duck quack
Combining words to make sentences

Sentence punctuation – capital letters and full stops (or ? or ! if appropriate)

Grammar and Punctuation Test 6 (page 18)

1 an exclamation mark   **1 mark**
Exclamation marks to demarcate sentences

2 **1 mark for both words correct**
(dark) (damp)
Word classes – adjectives

3 statements   **1 mark**
Statements – function and grammatical patterns

4 **1 mark for both full stops in the correct place**
We played hide and seek in the hall. Erin hid first.
Full stops to demarcate sentences

5 a gold ring   **1 mark**
Expanded noun phrases

6 On Friday, we had our breakfast early.

☑   **1 mark**

Word classes – verbs

7 a comma   **1 mark**
Commas to separate items in a list

8 **1 mark for both words correct**
(sailing) (watching)
Verb tenses – progressive form of past tense

9 **1 mark for an answer that explains that it is a contraction or shortened form.** e.g.
because there is a missing letter
It's is short for it is.
Apostrophes in contracted forms

10 a) I put all my work in a fol**der**.   **1 mark**
   b) a noun   **1 mark**
     Suffixes – forming nouns using –*ness*, –*ment*, –*er*

Grammar and Punctuation Test 7 (page 22)

1 or   **1 mark**
Co-ordinating conjunctions – *and, but, or*

2 (feels)   **1 mark**
Word classes – verbs

3 **1 mark for a recognisable/correctly formed question mark**
How do spiders make their webs**?**
Question marks to demarcate sentences

4 **1 mark for all joined correctly**

Word	Suffix
sad	ness
excite	ment
wicked	

Suffixes – forming nouns using –*ness*, –*ment*, –*er*

5 commands   **1 mark**
Commands – function and grammatical patterns

6 Last year I went to the fair for my birthday.   **1 mark**
Capital letters to demarcate sentences and for the word *I*

7 a noun   **1 mark**
Word classes – nouns

8 **1 mark for all three correct**

Sentence	Past tense	Present tense
Mum cleans the windows.		✓
Dad washed the dishes.	✓	
Khalid made his bed.	✓	

Verb tenses – simple past and present tense

9 **1 mark for a recognisable apostrophe between the correct letters**
T h o s e a r e R y a n's t o y s.
Apostrophe for possession

10 **2 marks for an appropriate and correctly formed statement, which also starts with a capital letter and ends with a full stop.** e.g.
The elephant had a long trunk.

1 mark for an appropriate and correctly formed statement, which does not have the necessary capital letter and/or full stop. e.g.
I liked the elephant best
there was a baby elephant

0 marks for statements that are not complete or correctly formed, or sentences that are not statements. e.g.
Elephant drink water.
Do you like elephants?
What a big elephant I saw!

Statements – function and grammatical pattern
Sentence punctuation – capital letters and full stops to demarcate sentences

Grammar and Punctuation Test 8 (page 24)

1 a question   **1 mark**
Questions – function and grammatical patterns

2 an adjective   **1 mark**
Word classes – adjectives

3 **un**lock   **1 mark**
Prefixes – how *un–* changes verbs and adjectives

4 (india)   **1 mark**
Capital letters for names of people and places

5 How creamy this ice cream is!   **1 mark**
Exclamation marks to demarcate sentences

6 a little puppy   **1 mark**
Expanded noun phrases

7 (fairly)   **1 mark**
Word classes – adverbs

8 Dan holds on to the rope and pulls.   **1 mark**
Tense consistency – simple present tense

9 **1 mark for a verb in the progressive (–ing) form that fits the sentence.** e.g.
reading, holding, finding
Note: the word must be spelt correctly.
Verb tenses – progressive form of past tense

10 a) **1 mark for a recognisable apostrophe between the letters *I* and *v***
    N o w I've f o u n d l o t s o f s h e l l s.
   b) **1 mark for a recognisable apostrophe between the letters *e* and *s* in *he's***
    D e v p l a y s m a r b l e s a n d he's g o o d.
    Apostrophes in contracted forms

Answers

Grammar and Punctuation Test 9 (page 26)

1 if **1 mark**
Subordinating conjunctions – *when, if, that, because*

2 My brother likes grapes. He has them for a snack. **1 mark**
Capital letters and full stops to demarcate sentences

3 an adjective **1 mark**
Word classes – adjectives

4 suffix **1 mark**
The term *suffix*

5 **1 mark for a recognisable comma after *twigs***
Collect some twigs, grass and leaves from the garden.
Commas to separate items in a list

6 **1 mark for all three correct**
Are you coming to see the new slide?
There are five tents in the field.
Do you want to play cricket?
Question marks and full stops to demarcate sentences

7 **1 mark for both words correct**
(chair) (tree)
Word classes – nouns

8 an exclamation **1 mark**
Exclamations – function and grammatical patterns

9 **1 mark for all three correct**

Sentence	Past tense	Present tense
Mum was painting the fence.	✓	
I am sweeping the path.		✓
Jo is looking for her football.		✓

Verb tenses – progressive form of present and past tense

10 **2 marks for an appropriate, correctly formed command, starting with a verb, that has correct punctuation (capital letter and full stop – or capital letter and exclamation mark).** e.g.
Tidy away your things.
Put your books away.
Stop what you are doing!

1 mark for an appropriate, correctly formed command, starting with a verb but with incorrect or no punctuation. e.g.
stop what you are doing

0 marks for sentences that are not commands even if correctly punctuated. e.g.
I want you to tidy your things away.
Are you ready?

Commands – function and grammatical pattern
Sentence punctuation – capital letters and full stops (or exclamation marks) to demarcate sentences

Grammar and Punctuation Test 10 (page 30)

1 **1 mark for both words correct**
(we) (sunday)
Capital letters for days of the week and to start sentences

2 **1 mark for all three correct**

Sentence	and	but
I have a sister .... a baby brother.	✓	
I can swim .... not very well.		✓
I like singing .... dancing.	✓	

Co-ordinating conjunctions – *and, but, or*

3 **1 mark for both words correct**
(twigs) (wind)
Word classes – nouns

4 **1 mark for all three correct**

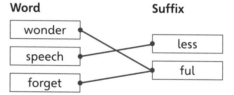

Word   Suffix

Suffixes – forming adjectives using *–ful* and *–less*

5 How clever you are to know the answer! **1 mark**
Exclamation marks to demarcate sentences

6 a statement **1 mark**
Statements – function and grammatical pattern

7 a comma **1 mark**
Commas to separate items in a list

8 **1 mark for any adverb that fits the sentence.** e.g.
sweetly, loudly, softly
Note: the word must be spelt correctly.
Word classes – adverbs

9 It hasn't rained for weeks. **1 mark**
Apostrophes in contracted forms

10 a) **1 mark for one simple past-tense verb that fits the sentence.** e.g.
ate, had, made
Note: the word must be spelt correctly.

b) **1 mark for one simple past-tense verb that fits the sentence.** e.g.
washed, cleaned, polished, drove
Note: the word must be spelt correctly.

Verb tenses – simple past tense

Grammar and Punctuation Test 11 (page 32)

1 that **1 mark**
Subordinating conjunctions – *when, if, that, because*

2 (silently) **1 mark**
Word classes – adverbs

3 **1 mark for both words correct**
(on) (molly)
Capital letters to start sentences and for names of people

4 an exclamation **1 mark**
Exclamations – function and grammatical pattern

5 The farmer is feeding the pigs. **1 mark**
Verb tenses – progressive form of present tense

6 **1 mark for both words correct**
(caught) (put)
Word classes – verbs

7 The Granger family went to the park. Roma rode her bike and Theo took his kite. **1 mark**
Full stops – demarcating sentences

8 **1 mark for all correct**

Noun	Singular	Plural
glass	✓	
vase	✓	
bricks		✓
dishes		✓

Plural noun suffixes –*s* and –*es*
The terms *singular* and *plural*

9 **1 mark for an answer that explains that it shows possession.** e.g.
because the coat belongs to Adam
because it is his coat
Apostrophe for possession

10 **2 marks for an appropriate and correctly formed question, which also starts with a capital letter and ends with a question mark.** e.g.
Where is my bag?
Have you seen my bag?
Can you help me find my bag?

1 mark for an appropriate and correctly formed question, which does not have the necessary capital letter and/or question mark. e.g.
Where did I put my bag.
do you have my bag

0 marks if the sentence does not fit the context, does not make sense or is not a question. e.g.
Is it time for school?
Where my bag?
Find my bag for me.

Questions – function and grammatical pattern
Sentence punctuation – capital letters and question marks to demarcate questions/sentences

Grammar and Punctuation Test 12 (page 34)

1 a question mark **1 mark**
Question marks to demarcate sentences

2 est **1 mark**
Suffixes – forming adjectives using –*er* and –*est*

3 **1 mark for both words correct**
(fresh) (brown)
Word classes – adjectives

4 a command **1 mark**
Commands – function and grammatical pattern

5 a box with a lid **1 mark**
Expanded noun phrases

6 a verb **1 mark**
Word classes – verbs

7 **1 mark for a recognisable comma after** *bread*
We need to buy some bread, vegetables and eggs from the farm shop.
Commas to separate items in a list

8 Dad takes Mila to school. **1 mark**
Verb tenses – simple present tense

9 **1 mark for** *don't* **spelt correctly with a recognisable apostrophe in the correct place**
I don't think these slippers will fit me.
Apostrophes in contracted forms

10 **2 marks for an appropriate and correctly formed statement, which also starts with a capital letter and ends with a full stop.** e.g.
I have got a cat.
My new dog is very cute.

1 mark for an appropriate and correctly formed statement, which does not have the necessary capital letter and/or full stop. e.g.
i have a new cat
my new dog is cute

0 marks for statements that are not complete or are incorrectly formed, or sentences that are not statements. e.g.
My new dog.
Do you like my cat?

Statements – function and grammatical pattern
Sentence punctuation – capital letters and full stops to demarcate sentences

Grammar and Punctuation Test 13 (page 38)

1 **1 mark for both words correct**
(clever) (brighter)
Word classes – adjectives

2 You can make a paper lantern. **1 mark**
Statements – function and grammatical pattern

3 The man walked slowly up the hill. **1 mark**
Word classes – adverbs
Use of –*ly* to turn adjectives into adverbs

Answers

Test 13 (page 38) continued

4 an exclamation mark   **1 mark**
Exclamation marks to demarcate sentences

5 **1 mark for an answer that explains that the words start with a capital letter because they are names.** e.g.
They are all names.
They are names of people and places.
Names and the days of the week need a capital letter.
Capital letters for names of people, places and days of the week

6 a comma   **1 mark**
Commas to separate items in a list

7 (when)   **1 mark**
Subordinating conjunctions – *when, if, that, because*

8 **1 mark for all three correct**
(Bees) (garden) (flowers)
Word classes – nouns

9 Nadias cakes had lots of cherries in them.
   ↑
  ☑   **1 mark**
Apostrophe for possession

10 **a)** **1 mark for a verb in the present progressive form that fits the sentence.** e.g.
making, baking, cooking
Note: the word must be spelt correctly.
Verb tenses – progressive form of present tense

   b) **1 mark for a verb in the simple past tense form that fits the sentence.** e.g.
planted, picked, grew
Note: the word must be spelt correctly.
Verb tenses – simple past tense

Grammar and Punctuation Test 14 (page 40)

1 an adverb   **1 mark**
Word classes – adverbs

2 <u>un</u>tidy   **1 mark**
Prefixes – how *un–* changes verbs and adjectives

3 **1 mark for both full stops identified correctly**
In the garden⊙there are lots of pots.
They are full of plants⊙with lots of flowers.
Granny helped us⊙to plant the flowers.
Full stops to demarcate sentences

4 **1 mark for all three correct**

Sentence	Question	Exclamation
What a cold day it is today		✓
How did you find me	✓	
How clean this floor is		✓

Function of sentences – questions and exclamations

5 I was so tired that I fell fast asleep.   **1 mark**
Subordinating conjunctions – *when, if, that, because*

6 We saw lions, tigers, zebras and apes at the safari park.   **1 mark**
Commas to separate items in a list

7 (gobbles)   **1 mark**
Tense consistency – simple past and present tense

8 **1 mark for an expanded noun phrase that fits the sentence/describes the item.** e.g.
a *big hat/a hat with a flower/a straw hat*
Expanded noun phrases to describe

9 (left)   **1 mark**
Word classes – verbs

10 **1 mark for *I've* spelt correctly with a recognisable apostrophe in the correct place**
<u>I've</u> missed you.

   1 mark for *I'll* spelt correctly with a recognisable apostrophe in the correct place
<u>I'll</u> write again soon.

Apostrophes in contracted forms

Grammar and Punctuation Test 15 (page 42)

1 a noun   **1 mark**
Word classes – nouns

2 **1 mark for all three correct**

Sentence	Full stop	Question mark
When will the coach leave		✓
When are we going to the swimming pool		✓
When it is wet, we have to play indoors	✓	

Full stops and question marks to demarcate sentences

3 **1 mark for both correct**
look(ed) amaze(ment)
Suffixes added to words
The term *suffix*

4 Keep your dog on a lead.   **1 mark**
Commands – function and grammatical pattern

5 I brushed my teeth **and** then I got dressed. **1 mark**
Co-ordinating conjunctions – *and, but, or*

6 **1 mark for all three correct**
(poor) (small) (lonely)
Word classes – adjectives

7 I think Poppy lives by the shops in
Clifton Street. **1 mark**
Capital letters for names of people and places

8 (is) **1 mark**
Verb tense – simple present tense

9 **1 mark for a recognisable apostrophe between**
t **and** *s* **in** *cats*
My cat's kittens are so tiny.
Apostrophe for possession

10 **2 marks for an appropriate, correctly formed**
exclamation that starts with *What* **or** *How* **and**
ends with an exclamation mark. e.g.
What a great jumper it is!
How lovely the colour is!

1 mark for an appropriate, correctly formed
exclamation, starting with *What* **or** *How* **but with**
no exclamation mark. e.g.
What a warm jumper it is.

0 marks for incomplete sentences (with no verb)
or sentences that are not exclamations even if
correctly punctuated. e.g.
Do you like my jumper?
What a jumper!

Exclamations – function and grammatical pattern
Exclamation marks to demarcate sentences

Grammar and Punctuation Test 16 (page 46)

1 an adverb **1 mark**
Word classes – adverbs

2 an exclamation mark **1 mark**
Exclamation marks to demarcate sentences

3 bright**ness** **1 mark**
Suffixes – forming nouns using *–ness, –ment, –er*

4 a statement **1 mark**
Statements – function and grammatical pattern

5 **1 mark for both correct**
(was) (took)
Word classes – verbs

6 **1 mark for both additional words circled**
(i) (manchester)
Capital letters for *I*, names of people and places
and to demarcate sentences

7 **1 mark for a recognisable comma after** *blue*.
You will need light blue, green and yellow
paper to make this colourful mask.
Commas to separate items in a list

8 (lets) **1 mark**
Apostrophes in contracted forms

9 **1 mark for all three correct**

Sentence	Past tense	Present tense
Dolly found an interesting pebble.	✓	
Henry packs his bag for school.		✓
Dad peels apples for the pie.		✓

Verb tenses – simple past and present tense

10 a) **1 mark for an expanded noun phrase that fits**
the sentence/describes the butterfly. e.g.
a blue butterfly
a butterfly with yellow wings
a pretty butterfly

0 marks for incomplete phrases or phrases that
do not describe. e.g.
blue butterfly
a butterfly

b) **1 mark for an expanded noun phrase that fits**
the sentence/describes the caterpillar. e.g.
a green caterpillar
a caterpillar with black spots
a little caterpillar

0 marks for incomplete phrases or phrases
that do not describe. e.g.
caterpillar
Expanded noun phrases to describe or specify

Grammar and Punctuation Test 17 (page 48)

1 **1 mark for both correct**
Should I start now
How was the film
Question marks to demarcate sentences

2 (because) **1 mark**
Subordinating conjunctions – *when, if, that, because*

3 exclamations **1 mark**
Exclamations – function and grammatical pattern

4 **1 mark for all three correct**
(giraffe) (legs) (human)
Word classes – nouns

5 Megan's new car has four doors. **1 mark**
Apostrophe for possession

6 **1 mark for any plausible adverb that fits the**
sentence. e.g.
slowly, quickly, suddenly, smoothly
Note: the word must be spelt correctly.
Word classes – adverbs

7 (walked) **1 mark**
Tense consistency – maintaining present tense

8 **1 mark for all three correct**
boats, coaches, bikes
Plural noun suffixes *–s* or *–es*
The terms *singular* and *plural*

Answers

Test 17 (page 48) continued

9 **1 mark for both full stops identified correctly**
I was waiting⊙at the bus stop. I saw the bus⊙ coming round the corner. My friend Mo was running⊙for the bus. Mo was late.
Full stops to demarcate sentences

10 **2 marks for an appropriate, correctly formed command, starting with a verb, that starts with a capital letter and ends with a full stop or an exclamation mark.** e.g.
Put your coat on.
Don't forget your coat!
Take your coat with you.

1 mark for an appropriate, correctly formed command, starting with a verb but with incorrect or no punctuation. e.g.
Take your coat
put a warm coat on

0 marks for sentences that are not commands even if correctly punctuated. e.g.
You will need your coat today.
Have you got your coat?

Commands – function and grammatical pattern

Capital letters and full stops (or exclamation marks) to demarcate sentences

Grammar and Punctuation Test 18 (page 50)

1 a command **1 mark**
Commands – function and grammatical pattern

2 **1 mark for all three correct**

Sentence	ful	less
If it rains an umbrella is very use......	✓	
Charlie was feeling bored and rest......		✓
It is good to be help......	✓	

Suffixes – forming adjectives using –*ful* and –*less*

3 **1 mark for any plausible adjective that fits the sentence.** e.g.
strong, noisy, cold
Note: the word must be spelt correctly.

0 marks for a word that is not an adjective even if it makes sense. e.g.
stopping

Word classes – adjectives

4 (were) **1 mark**
Verb tenses – progressive form of past tense

5 **1 mark for all three correct**
(miss) (atkins) (monday)
Capital letters for names of people and days of the week

6 Mum was waiting when Toby came home. **1 mark**
Tense consistency – maintaining past tense

7 **1 mark for all three correct**
(melted) (fell) (landed)
Word classes – verbs

8 **1 mark for both correct**
Lucy⊙and I like to collect toy⊙cars, coins, shells⊙and stickers.
Commas to separate items in a list

9 **1 mark for *wouldn't* spelt correctly with a recognisable apostrophe in the correct place**
The tap **wouldn't** turn off.
Apostrophes in contracted forms

10 a) **1 mark for an appropriate and complete sentence, which follows on from the word *or*.** e.g.
We must walk quickly or we will be late.
We must walk quickly or miss the bus.

b) **1 mark for an appropriate and complete sentence, which follows on from the word *but*.** e.g.
I have got my bag but I forgot my book.
I have got my bag but it is heavy.
Co-ordinating conjunctions – *and, but, or*

Spelling tests

Spelling Test 1 (page 4)

1 shock **1 mark**
/k/ sound spelt 'ck'

2 stone **1 mark**
Vowel digraphs – o–e

3 body **1 mark**
Words ending in –*y*

4 asked **1 mark**
Adding –*ing*, –*ed*, –*er* to verbs (no change in spelling)

5 sly **1 mark**
/i–e/ sound spelt 'y' at the end of words

6 taller **1 mark**
/or/ sound spelt 'a' before *l, ll*
Adding –*er* and –*est* (no change in spelling)

7 stage **1 mark**
/j/ sound spelt 'ge' or 'dge' at the end of words

8 wasp **1 mark**
/o/ sound spelt 'a' after *w* and *qu*

9 Wednesday **1 mark**
Days of the week

10 write **1 mark**
/r/ sound spelt 'wr' at the beginning of words
Homophones

11 scaring **1 mark**
Adding –*ing*, –*ed*, –*er*, –*est*, –*y* to words ending in –*e*
Vowel trigraphs – *are*

12 fiction **1 mark**
Words ending in –*tion*

Spelling Test 2 (page 12)

1 give   1 mark
/v/ sound at the end of words spelt 've'

2 skid   1 mark
/k/ sound spelt 'k'

3 shirt   1 mark
Vowel digraphs – ir

4 dream   1 mark
Vowel digraphs – ea

5 softest   1 mark
Adding –er and –est to adjectives (no change
in spelling)

6 space   1 mark
/s/ sound spelt 'c'

7 cover   1 mark
/u/ sound spelt 'o'

8 honey   1 mark
/ee/ sound spelt 'ey'

9 blew   1 mark
Homophones
Vowel digraphs – ew

10 shoppers   1 mark
Adding –ing, –ed, –er, –est, –y to words ending
in a single consonant after a single vowel
Adding –s and –es to words

11 candle   1 mark
'–le' spelling at the end of words

12 careless   1 mark
Adding the suffixes –ment, –ness, –ful, –less, –ly
Vowel trigraphs – are

Spelling Test 3 (page 20)

1 sniff   1 mark
/f/ sound spelt 'ff'

2 party   1 mark
Words ending in –y
Vowel digraphs – ar

3 proud   1 mark
Vowel digraphs – ou

4 shapes   1 mark
Adding –s and –es to words
Vowel digraphs – a-e

5 classroom   1 mark
Compound words

6 feather   1 mark
Vowel digraphs – ea, er

7 kneel   1 mark
/n/ sound spelt 'kn'

8 chalk   1 mark
/or/ sound spelt 'a' before l, ll, lk

9 warning   1 mark
/or/ sound spelt 'ar' after w
Adding –ing, –ed, –er (no change in spelling)

10 travel   1 mark
'–el' spelling at the end of words

11 funniest   1 mark
Adding –ed, –ing, –er, –est to words ending
consonant –y

12 busy   1 mark
Common exception words

Spelling Test 4 (page 28)

1 float   1 mark
Vowel digraphs – oa

2 patch   1 mark
'tch' spelling

3 market   1 mark
Vowel digraphs – ar

4 thicker   1 mark
Adding –er and –est to adjectives (no change
in spelling)
/k/ sound spelt 'ck'

5 trying   1 mark
Adding –ed, –ing, –er, –est to words ending in –y
/ie/ sound spelt 'y' at the end of words

6 worm   1 mark
/er/ sound spelt 'or' after w

7 while   1 mark
/w/ sound spelt 'wh'

8 wreck   1 mark
/r/ sound spelt 'wr'

9 crazy   1 mark
Adding –ing, –ed, –er, –est, –y to words ending in –e

10 donkeys   1 mark
/ee/ sound spelt 'ey'

11 medal   1 mark
'–al' spelling at the end of words

12 measure   1 mark
/zh/ sound spelt 's'

Spelling Test 5 (page 36)

1 blink   1 mark
'nk' spelling

2 bright   1 mark
Vowel trigraphs – igh

3 hear   1 mark
Homophones
Vowel trigraphs – ear

4 playground   1 mark
Compound words
Vowel digraphs – ay, ou

Answers

Spelling Test 5 (page 36) continued

5 crosses — **1 mark**
Adding –s and –es to nouns and verbs

6 fridge — **1 mark**
/j/ sound spelt 'ge' and 'dge' at the end of words

7 month — **1 mark**
/u/ sound spelt 'o'

8 graph — **1 mark**
/f/ sound spelt 'ph'

9 watch — **1 mark**
/o/ sound spelt 'a' after *w* and *qu*

10 puddle — **1 mark**
'–le' spelling at the end of words

11 babies — **1 mark**
Adding –es to nouns and verbs ending in –y

12 graceful — **1 mark**
Adding the suffixes –ment, –ness, –ful, –less, –ly
/s/ sound spelt 'c'

Spelling Test 6 (page 44)

1 glue — **1 mark**
Vowel digraphs – *ue*

2 weak — **1 mark**
Vowel digraphs – *ea*
Homophones

3 solve — **1 mark**
/v/ sound spelt 've' at the end of words

4 sketch — **1 mark**
/k/ sound spelt 'k'
'tch' spelling

5 drinking — **1 mark**
Adding –ing, –ed, –er to verbs (no change in spelling)
'nk' spelling

6 fancy — **1 mark**
/s/ sound spelt 'c' before *e*, *i* and *y*

7 dripping — **1 mark**
Adding –ing, –ed, –er, –est, –y to words ending in
a single consonant

8 pencil — **1 mark**
'–il' spelling at the end of words
/s/ sound spelt 'c'

9 squash — **1 mark**
/o/ sound spelt 'a' after *w* and *qu*

10 towards — **1 mark**
/or/ sound spelt 'ar' after *w*

11 hurried — **1 mark**
Adding –ed, –ing, –er, –est to words ending in
consonant –y

12 people — **1 mark**
Common exception words

Spelling Test 7 (page 52)

1 fizz — **1 mark**
/z/ sound spelt 'zz'

2 burst — **1 mark**
Vowel digraphs – *ur*

3 knock — **1 mark**
/n/ sound spelt 'kn'

4 lolly — **1 mark**
Words ending in –y

5 limped — **1 mark**
Adding –ed to verbs (no change in spelling)

6 fry — **1 mark**
/ie/ sound spelt 'y' at the end of words

7 upstairs — **1 mark**
Compound words
Vowel trigraphs – *air*

8 kettle — **1 mark**
'–le' spelling at the end of words
/k/ sound spelt 'k'

9 half — **1 mark**
Common exception words

10 worth — **1 mark**
/er/ sound spelt 'or' after *w*

11 carries — **1 mark**
Adding –es to nouns and verbs ending in –y

12 tasteless — **1 mark**
Adding the suffixes –ment, –ness, –ful, –less, –ly
Vowel digraphs – *a–e*

This book of answers is a pull-out section from **KS1 SATs Grammar, Punctuation and Spelling 10-Minute Tests.**

Published by **Schofield & Sims Ltd**, 7 Mariner Court, Wakefield, West Yorkshire WF4 3FL, UK
Telephone 01484 607080
www.schofieldandsims.co.uk

This edition copyright © Schofield & Sims Ltd, 2019
First published in 2019
Second impression 2020

Author: **Carol Matchett**
Carol Matchett has asserted her moral rights under the Copyright, Designs and Patents Act, 1988, to be identified as the author of this work.

British Library Cataloguing in Publication Data
A catalogue record for this book is available from the British Library.

Design by **Ledgard Jepson**
Printed in the UK by **Page Bros (Norwich) Ltd**

ISBN 978 07217 1499 8

7 We had to wait for a ....

1 mark

8 The diver found the .... of a ship.

1 mark

9 Ben had this .... idea.

1 mark

10 I saw two .... in the field.

1 mark

11 He won the gold .... in the race.

1 mark

12 I used a ruler to .... the line.

1 mark

Total marks ....

Grammar and Punctuation Test **10**

1   Circle **two** words that need a **capital letter** in the sentence below.

we set off very early on sunday morning to catch

the train.

2   Tick the correct word to complete each sentence.

Sentence	and	but
I have a sister .... a baby brother.		
I can swim .... not very well.		
I like singing .... dancing.		

3   Circle the **two nouns** in the sentence below.

Sometimes you can hear twigs snapping when the

wind blows outside.

4   Draw a line to match each word to the **suffix** that turns it into an adjective. You can use a suffix more than once.

Word

| wonder |
| speech |
| forget |

Suffix

| less |
| ful |

5   Write the missing punctuation mark to complete the sentence below.

How clever you are to know the answer......................

6 What type of sentence is below? Tick **one**.

Last weekend, Ellie's family went to the cinema.

a question ☐   an exclamation ☐

a statement ☐   a command ☐

☐
1 mark

7 Which punctuation mark is needed in the sentence below? Tick **one**.

Would you like some red grapes an apple or a banana?

a full stop ☐   an exclamation mark ☐

a comma ☐   an apostrophe ☐

☐
1 mark

8 Write **one adverb** to complete the sentence below.

The children sang ....

☐
1 mark

9 Which sentence uses an **apostrophe** correctly? Tick **one**.

It has'nt rained for weeks. ☐

It hasn't rained for weeks. ☐

It hasnt' rained for weeks. ☐

It hasnt rained for week's. ☐

☐
1 mark

10 Write **one verb** to complete each sentence.

a) Yesterday I .... egg sandwiches for lunch.

b) Last week, Dad and I .... the car.

☐
2 marks

Total marks .... Time taken ....

Grammar and Punctuation Test 11

1 Tick **one** word to complete the sentence below.

I thought .... it might snow today.

when ☐   if ☐   that ☐   because ☐

☐
1 mark

2 Circle the **adverb** in the sentence below.

In the wild, tigers hunt silently at night.

☐
1 mark

3 Circle **two** words that need a **capital letter** in the sentence below.

on a sunny day, we go to town to meet my

friend molly.

☐
1 mark

4 What type of sentence is below? The end punctuation is hidden.

How wonderful it is to see you again▮

Tick **one**.

a statement ☐   a question ☐

a command ☐   an exclamation ☐

☐
1 mark

5 Which sentence shows what the farmer is doing <u>now</u>? Tick **one**.

The farmer drove the tractor. ☐

The farmer is feeding the pigs. ☐

The farmer called the sheepdog. ☐

The farmer was milking the cows. ☐

☐
1 mark

6 Circle the **two verbs** in the sentence below.

I caught three fish and put them in the fishing net.

1 mark

7 Add a **full stop** in the correct place below.

The Granger family went to the park Roma rode her bike and Theo took his kite.

1 mark

8 Tick to show whether each noun is **singular** or **plural**.

Noun	Singular	Plural
glass		
vase		
bricks		
dishes		

1 mark

9 Why does the underlined word have an **apostrophe**?

I think <u>Adam's</u> coat is blue.

....

....

1 mark

10 Abdul can't find his bag.

Write a **question** he could ask his mum to help him find it.
Remember to use correct punctuation.

....

....

2 marks

Total marks .... Time taken ....

Grammar and Punctuation Test 12

1   Look at where the arrow is pointing.

Will you write to me soon I hope you will.

Which punctuation mark is missing? Tick **one**.

a full stop ☐   a question mark ☐

a comma ☐   an apostrophe ☐

☐ *1 mark*

---

2   Tick **one suffix** needed to complete the sentence below.

The big dog barked the loud................... of all.

er ☐   ly ☐   est ☐   ness ☐

☐ *1 mark*

---

3   Circle the **two adjectives** in the sentence below.

Take a slice of fresh brown bread and spread it with butter.

☐ *1 mark*

---

4   What type of sentence is below?

Leave the building at once if you hear the fire alarm.

Tick **one**.

a statement ☐   a question ☐

a command ☐   an exclamation ☐

☐ *1 mark*

---

5   Tick **one noun phrase** below.

quite quickly ☐   very powerful ☐

a box with a lid ☐   feeling tired ☐

☐ *1 mark*

6 What type of word is underlined in the sentence below?

I saw two birds <u>land</u> on the fence over by the trees.

Tick **one**.

a noun ☐ an adjective ☐ a verb ☐ an adverb ☐ ☐

1 mark

7 Add a **comma** to the sentence below in the correct place.

We need to buy some bread vegetables and eggs from the farm shop. ☐

1 mark

8 Which sentence is written in the **present tense**? Tick **one**.

Dad told Mila a story. ☐

Dad takes Mila to school. ☐

Dad gave Mila a birthday card. ☐

Dad sang Mila a song. ☐ ☐

1 mark

9 Write the words <u>do not</u> as one word, using an **apostrophe**.

I .... think these slippers will fit me. ☐

1 mark

10 Josh is telling Ravi about his new pet.

Write a **statement** that Josh might say. Remember to use correct punctuation.

....

.... ☐

2 marks

Total marks .... Time taken ....

Spelling Test 5

The adult who is helping you will read the sentences and tell you the missing words.

1   The smoke made me .... my eyes.

2   Amy likes to wear .... colours.

3   I can .... something outside.

4   The children ran into the ....

5   Zara .... the road at the lights.

6   I put the milk in the ....

7 Claire was born in the .... of May.

☐ 1 mark

8 We drew a .... to show the birds we saw.

☐ 1 mark

9 Mr Lewis looked at his ....

☐ 1 mark

10 The rain made a .... on the floor.

☐ 1 mark

11 All the .... began to cry.

☐ 1 mark

12 The swan looked very ....

☐ 1 mark

Total marks ....

Grammar and Punctuation Test 13

1 Circle the **two adjectives** in the sentence below.

The clever fox knew the sun was brighter than the moon

1 mark

2 Which sentence is a **statement**? Tick **one**.

You can make a paper lantern. ☐

First, take the piece of paper. ☐

Fold the paper in half. ☐

Cut along the dotted lines. ☐

1 mark

3 Add a **suffix** to the word <u>slow</u> to make it into an **adverb**.

The man walked slow............... up the hill.

1 mark

4 Which punctuation mark completes the sentence below?

How kind of you to remember my birthday

Tick **one**.

a full stop ☐   a question mark ☐

a comma ☐   an exclamation mark ☐

1 mark

5 Why do the underlined words start with a **capital letter**?

<u>Ms Roy</u> took her class to <u>Tamworth Castle</u> on <u>Tuesday</u> morning.

....

....

1 mark

6 Which punctuation mark is needed in the sentence below?

Giraffes eat leaves twigs and fruit from the tops of trees.

Tick **one**.

an apostrophe ☐   a full stop ☐

a comma ☐   an exclamation mark ☐

☐
1 mark

7 Circle **one** word in the sentence below that can be replaced with the word <u>if</u>.

My   bike   goes   fast   when   I   pedal   hard.

☐
1 mark

8 Circle the **three nouns** in the sentence below.

Bees   often   come   into   our   garden   to   feed   on   the

brightly   coloured   flowers.

☐
1 mark

9 Tick **one** box to show where an **apostrophe** is needed in the sentence below.

Nadias cakes had lots of cherries in them.

☐   ☐   ☐   ☐

☐
1 mark

10 Write **one verb** to complete what each child is saying.

a) Today I am .... some cakes.

b) Yesterday, I .... some flowers.

☐
2 marks

Total marks ....   Time taken ....

Grammar and Punctuation Test 14

1 What type of word is underlined in the sentence below? Tick **one**.

He placed the glass of water <u>carefully</u> on the tray.

a noun ☐ an adjective ☐ a verb ☐ an adverb ☐ ☐

1 mark

2 Add **two** letters to the word <u>tidy</u> to complete the sentence below.

My sister's bedroom is always a mess because she is so

...................tidy. ☐

1 mark

3 Circle the **full stops** that are in the wrong places. One has been done for you.

In the garden⊙there are lots of pots . They are full of plants .

with lots of flowers . Granny helped us . to plant the flowers. ☐

1 mark

4 Tick to show whether each sentence is a **question** or an **exclamation**. The end punctuation is hidden.

Sentence	Question	Exclamation
What a cold day it is today░		
How did you find me░		
How clean this floor is░		

☐

1 mark

5 Which sentence is correct? Tick **one**.

I was so tired if I fell fast asleep. ☐

I was so tired that I fell fast asleep. ☐

I was so tired because I fell fast asleep. ☐

I was so tired or I fell fast asleep. ☐

☐

1 mark

6 Which sentence uses **commas** correctly? Tick **one**.

We saw lions, tigers, zebras, and apes, at the safari park. ☐

We saw lions, tigers, zebras, and apes at the safari park. ☐

We saw lions, tigers, zebras and apes at the safari park. ☐

We saw lions, tigers, zebras and apes, at the safari park. ☐

☐ 1 mark

7 The sentence below should be in the **past tense**. Circle **one** word that needs to be changed.

The dragon was hungry so he gobbles up all the food.

☐ 1 mark

8 Write a **noun phrase** to describe what you see in the picture.

The lady is wearing ....

☐ 1 mark

9 Circle the **verb** in the sentence below.

Harl left the house at eight o'clock this morning.

☐ 1 mark

10 Write the words in the box as one word, using an **apostrophe**. One has been done for you.

I am	........I'm........	so glad you can come to my party.
I have	....	missed you.
I will	....	write again soon.

☐ 2 marks

Total marks .... Time taken ....

Grammar and Punctuation Test 15

1 What type of word is underlined in the sentence below?

Granddad took a <u>sweet</u> from the packet.

Tick **one**.

a noun ☐   an adjective ☐   a verb ☐   an adverb ☐   ☐

1 mark

2 Tick the name of the punctuation mark that should complete each sentence.

Sentence	Full stop	Question mark
When will the coach leave		
When are we going to the swimming pool		
When it is wet, we have to play indoors		

☐

1 mark

3 Circle the **two suffixes** in the sentence below.

Nisha looked up in amazement at the moon in the night sky.

☐

1 mark

4 Which sentence is a **command**? Tick **one**.

We have a new dog.   ☐

Dogs need exercise.   ☐

Keep your dog on a lead.   ☐

Some dogs like to explore.   ☐   ☐

1 mark

5 Write **one** word to join the two ideas in the sentence below.   ☐

I brushed my teeth .... then I got dressed.

1 mark

6 Circle the **three adjectives** in the sentence below.

One day, a poor fisherman was sitting in his small,

lonely cottage by the sea.

1 mark

7 Which sentence uses capital letters correctly? Tick **one**.

I think poppy lives by the shops in Clifton street. ☐

I think poppy lives by the shops in Clifton street. ☐

I think Poppy lives by the shops in Clifton Street. ☐

I think Poppy lives by the Shops in clifton street. ☐

1 mark

8 Circle the word that shows the sentence below is in the **present tense**.

The sky is very dark.

1 mark

9 Write an **apostrophe** in the correct place in the sentence below.

My cats kittens are so tiny.

1 mark

10 Liz really likes her new jumper.

Write an **exclamation** that Liz could say about the jumper. Remember to use correct punctuation.

....

....

2 marks

Total marks .... Time taken ....

Spelling Test **6**

The adult who is helping you will read the sentences and tell you the missing words.

1 This .... is very sticky. ☐ 1 mark

2 I felt .... when I was ill. ☐ 1 mark

3 It was a tricky problem to .... ☐ 1 mark

4 Ruby drew a .... of her cat. ☐ 1 mark

5 I was .... a glass of water. ☐ 1 mark

6 We went to a .... dress party. ☐ 1 mark

7 The tap was .... into the bath.

1 mark

8 Write your name in ....

1 mark

9 Don't .... the cake.

1 mark

10 Take three steps .... me.

1 mark

11 The man .... on to the train.

1 mark

12 Lots of .... like dogs.

1 mark

Total marks ....

Grammar and Punctuation Test 16

1 What type of word is underlined in the sentence below?

The lid was stuck <u>firmly</u> on the jar.

Tick **one**.

a noun ☐   an adjective ☐   a verb ☐   an adverb ☐   ☐

---

2 Look at where the arrow is pointing.

What a mess you've made ↑ I can help you tidy up.

Which punctuation mark is missing? Tick **one**.

a comma ☐   a question mark ☐

a full stop ☐   an exclamation mark ☐   ☐

1 mark

---

3 Add a **suffix** to the word <u>bright</u> to complete the sentence below.

When I looked at the lights, I was dazzled by their

bright............... .   ☐

1 mark

---

4 What type of sentence is below?

One day, Emily decided to surprise her friends.

Tick **one**.

a question ☐   a statement ☐

a command ☐   an exclamation ☐   ☐

1 mark

---

5 Circle the **verbs** in the sentence below.

On Saturday, Anila was bored so Mum took the

family for a walk.   ☐

1 mark

6 Circle the words that need a **capital letter** in the sentence below. One has been done for you.

(we) had fun when i visited my friend in manchester.

☐ 1 mark

7 Add a **comma** to the sentence below in the correct place.

You will need light blue green and yellow paper to make this colourful mask.

☐ 1 mark

8 Circle the word that should have an **apostrophe** in the sentence below.

I have some beads so lets make a necklace.

☐ 1 mark

9 Tick to show whether each sentence is written in the **past tense** or the **present tense**.

Sentence	Past tense	Present tense
Dolly found an interesting pebble.		
Henry packs his bag for school.		
Dad peels apples for the pie.		

☐ 1 mark

10 **a)** Harry has seen a butterfly in the garden. Write a **noun phrase** he could use to tell his teacher what the butterfly looked like.

I saw ....

b) Jamila saw a caterpillar in the garden. Write a **noun phrase** she could use to tell her teacher what the caterpillar looked like.

I saw ....

☐ 2 marks

Total marks .... Time taken ....

Grammar and Punctuation Test 17

1   Tick the sentences that should end with a **question mark**.

Should I start now ☐

How was the film ☐

Stop right there ☐

☐
1 mark

2   Circle **one** word in the sentence below that can be replaced with the word <u>when</u>.

My little brother was scared because there was a storm. ☐

1 mark

3   Read the sentences below. The end punctuation is hidden.

What a brilliant party it was on Friday ▮
How happy everyone was ▮

Tick **one** word that describes these sentences.

statements ☐   commands ☐

questions ☐   exclamations ☐

☐
1 mark

4   Circle the **three** nouns in the sentence below.

A giraffe has long legs that can be taller than a human.

☐
1 mark

5   Which sentence uses an **apostrophe** correctly? Tick **one**.

Megans' new car has four doors. ☐

Megan's new car has four doors. ☐

Megans new car has four door's. ☐

Megans new car has four doors'. ☐

☐
1 mark

6 Write **one adverb** to complete the sentence below.

The lorry drove .... down the road.

1 mark

7 The sentence below should be in the **present tense**. Circle **one** word that needs to be changed.

Today, it is raining as Noah and his mum walked to school.

1 mark

8 Write each singular noun as a **plural noun**.

Singular	Plural
boat	....
coach	....
bike	....

1 mark

9 Circle the **full stops** that are in the wrong places. One has been done for you.

I was waiting⊙at the bus stop . I saw the bus . coming round the corner . My friend Mo was running . for the bus . Mo was late .

1 mark

10 It is a cold day. Leela's mum thinks Leela will need a coat.

Write a **command** that Leela's mum might say to Leela. Remember to use correct punctuation.

....

....

2 marks

Total marks .... Time taken ....

Grammar and Punctuation Test 18

1 What type of sentence is below?

Don't shut down the computer.

Tick **one**.

a statement ☐   a command ☐

a question ☐   an exclamation ☐

☐
1 mark

2 Tick the correct **suffix** to complete each sentence.

Sentence	ful	less
If it rains an umbrella is very use........... .		
Charlie was feeling bored and rest............ .		
It is good to be help............ .		

☐
1 mark

3 Write **one adjective** to complete the sentence below.

The wind was ....

☐
1 mark

4 Circle the word that shows the sentence below is in the **past tense**.

We were camping in a field by the sea.

☐
1 mark

5 Circle **three** words that need a **capital letter** in the sentence below.

miss atkins always meets her sister in town on

monday mornings.

☐
1 mark

6 Which sentence is correct? Tick **one**.

Mum was waiting when Toby comes home. ☐

Mum is waiting when Toby came home. ☐

Mum is waiting when Toby come home. ☐

Mum was waiting when Toby came home. ☐

☐ 1 mark

7 Circle all the **verbs** in the sentence below.

When the snow melted, it fell from the trees and landed on the ground below.

☐ 1 mark

8 Circle the **commas** that are in the wrong places. One has been done for you.

Lucy⊙and I like to collect toy , cars , coins , shells , and stickers.

☐ 1 mark

9 Write the words <u>would not</u> as one word, using an **apostrophe**.

The tap .... turn off.

☐ 1 mark

10 Jake and Asha are on their way to school.

Complete each sentence to show what they are saying.

a) We must walk quickly or ....

b) I have got my bag but ....

☐ 2 marks

Total marks .... Time taken ....

Spelling Test 7

The adult who is helping you will read the sentences and tell you the missing words.

1 The mixture began to ....

1 mark

2 The little boy .... his balloon.

1 mark

3 There was a .... at the door.

1 mark

4 I would like a red ice ....

1 mark

5 The girl .... over the line.

1 mark

6 You can .... fish in a pan.

1 mark

7 I went .... to bed.

☐ 1 mark

8 Dad boiled the .... to make tea.

☐ 1 mark

9 The bell rang at .... past three.

☐ 1 mark

10 How much is the picture ....?

☐ 1 mark

11 The woman .... the heavy case.

☐ 1 mark

12 The soup was ....

☐ 1 mark

Total marks ....

Progress chart: grammar and punctuation tests

Write the score (out of 11) for each grammar and punctuation test in the box provided to the right of the chart. Then colour the row next to the box to represent this score.

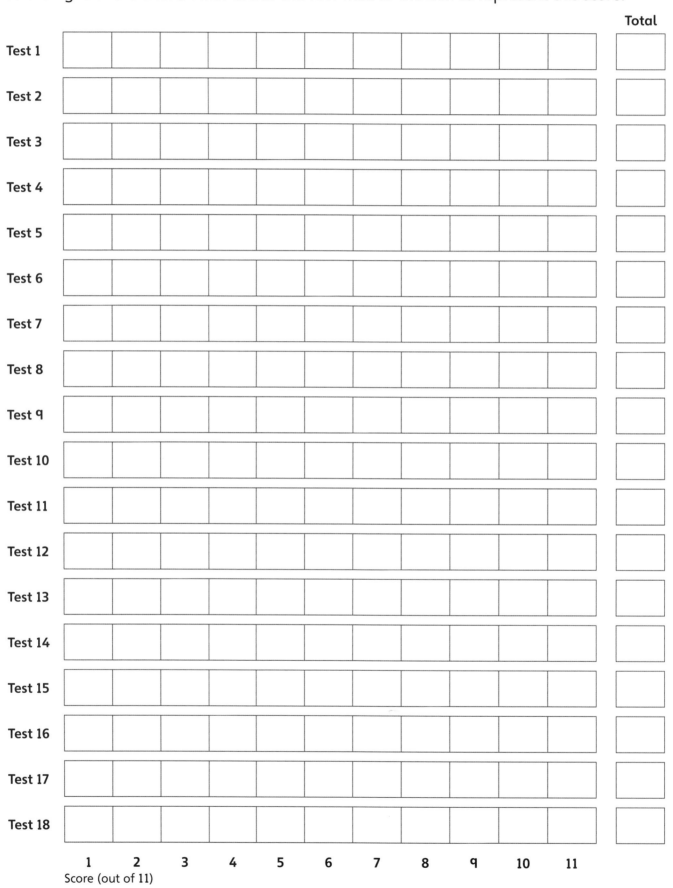

Score (out of 11)

Progress chart: spelling tests

Write the total score (out of 12) for each spelling test in the box provided to the right of the chart. Then colour the row next to the box to represent this score.

Test 1

Test 2

Test 3

Test 4

Test 5

Test 6

Test 7

Total

1   2   3   4   5   6   7   8   9   10   11   12

Score (out of 12)

Tricky spellings record sheet

Use this sheet to make a note of any spellings you find difficult. Refer back and practise the spellings until they are no longer difficult.

_____   _____

_____   _____

_____   _____

_____   _____

_____   _____

_____   _____

_____   _____

_____   _____

_____   _____

_____   _____

_____   _____

_____   _____

_____   _____

_____   _____

_____   _____

_____   _____

_____   _____

Schofield & Sims